THE SECRET SKETCHBOOK OF A BLOOMSBURY LADY

British Library Cataloguing
in Publication Data
Mahood, Kenneth
The secret sketchbook of
a Bloomsbury lady.
1. English wit and humor,
Pictorial
I. Title
741.5'942   NC1479

ISBN 0-370-30475 6

© Kenneth Mahood 1982
Foreword © The Bodley Head Limited 1982
Printed in Great Britain for
The Bodley Head Ltd
9 Bow Street, London WC2E 7AL
by William Clowes (Beccles) Ltd
First published 1982

KENNETH MAHOOD
The Secret Sketchbook of a
Bloomsbury Lady

FOREWORD BY MICHAEL HOLROYD

THE BODLEY HEAD
LONDON SYDNEY
TORONTO

Foreword by Michael Holroyd

In commissioning a Foreword to this important work, the Chairman and Directors of the Bodley Head have impressed on me the frightful responsibility which I am to pass on to you, the readers, whoever you are. The late Mrs Mahood's grandson has gained (I am told) a reputation for drawing funny sketches. He is Irish and has published some work in the *New Yorker*. Foreigners apparently enjoy these drawings and are said to find them amusing. Whatever the truth of these rumours, it is clear to the Trained Eye that "Ken" Mahood, who owns the lavish copyright in his grandmother's portfolios, has been up to something. Suddenly there is a familiarity about his work. Either he has acquired by some hereditary quirk a distorted echo of Maud Millicent Mahood's powerful line and eclectic vision; or he has for years been deliberately exploiting and exporting what amounts to a supply of family fakes, if not actual forgeries. This is not the place, nor have I the rank, to act on this information—I fancy we may all read about it soon enough in such newspapers as the *Daily Mail*. For reasons of his own, however, Mr Mahood has chosen further to confuse his *pastiches* with the *oeuvre* of the one Mahood worthy of the name by throwing into this book an unprofessional narrative of his own and then undermining these fine examples of original Bloomsbury field work with captions of such academic inexpertise that, unlike other authentic blooms of this industry, the work falls far short of the standard two volumes we all love and expect. It is to avoid the risk of the book being excluded from the student's list of required reading, or even of provoking smiles among the uninstructed General Reader (there is, I believe, one still left) that I have been asked to add to the price with some substantial sentences, a couple of weighty paragraphs, explaining the book's provenance and exposing its threadbare editing.

Maud Millicent Mahood's work, if not actually seen, has long been suspected. Rumours to the effect that there was more to come on Bloomsbury have not been lacking and have never been convincingly refuted. Nor was the influence of her characteristic style undetected by those who have studied the period, though references to this influence, in the absence of a *catalogue raisonné*, have been implied rather than supported by notes. Until this year Mrs Mahood's distinguished place had lain between the lines. Now, after the rude attentions of her poacher-grandson, she springs vulgarly to life before us. Of the editor's principles, of the commercial haphazardness with which he plucks from the poor dead woman's private diary some of the more shocking entries and sticks them to the gaudiest leaves from her confidential sketchbook, of all this I say absolutely nothing at all. It is to be hoped that the remaining material will be handed over to an educational institution personed by a proper team of professors. That there will be a considerable amount of investigation and commentary to be performed by these scholars I have no doubt; just as there already is some explaining away to be done by myself.

Lytton Strachey and Maud Mahood
by Henry Lamb

Maud Peeling Onions by Picasso

INTRODUCTION

More superfluous words have been written about the Bloomsbury Group, according to *The Guinness Book of Records*, than any other literary coterie in history. Fortunately, this sketchbook does not add to the surfeit, as my grandmother drew rather than wrote; but it does show the members in an entirely new light. Most of the drawings are of events that have apparently escaped the notice of all the other writers. Who else knew that Lytton Strachey had 'I LOVE DUNCAN, HENRY, OTTOLINE, DORA ETC.' (in mirror writing) tattooed on his chest? Or that Dora Carrington held an annual coach trip to the seaside for all the men who were in love with her?

Perhaps my grandmother's ability to catch the Group in their most private moments was due to her chameleon-like talent for blending into any background. She is not mentioned in any of the biographies, but when Virginia Woolf referred in her diary to 'that enigmatic mute of Bloomsbury', I believe she was writing about her. Born in 1880, my grandmother, Maud Millicent Mahood, was the daughter of Muldoon Mahood (known as Ireland's Oblomov) and his wife Isadore. Her father was something of a recluse; indeed their house at Downpatrick, Co. Down, could only be approached through a complex six-foot-high yew maze. Here my grandmother grew up a trifle

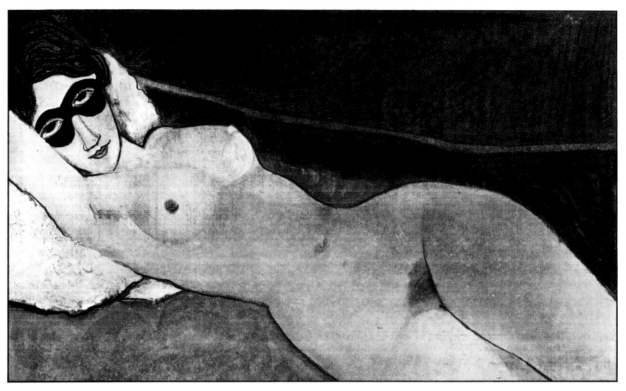

Maud Reclining by Modigliani

isolated from society—she was sixteen before she could find her way out unaided. When she did, she soon showed herself to be unconventional, demonstrating her drawing ability by chalking graffiti on the local cows. Lacking a direction to her life, she plunged into religion and managed to convert the parish priest to Buddhism. 'The poor man would have done anything to escape her confessions,' complained his bishop.

Eventually, much to her family's relief, she tired of evangelism and vanished to Europe to soak up culture, study art and attend fancy-dress balls. It was at one of these that she met the French poet Apollinaire, who introduced her to many of the artists who took over her life. She modelled for Rodin, chased frogs off water lilies for Monet and helped Rousseau with his backgrounds. To judge from contemporary portraits, she had a rather fey look. She had deep-set eyes, one blue and the other green, and her luminous, delicately parrot-shaped nose overhung a generous mouth which, when open, revealed a set of teeth like a gin-trap. Her clothes were rather extreme—often original designs made out of old potato sacks dyed in bright colours, which she wore with a group of old hatboxes tied to her shawl. It is widely believed that her appearance gave Picasso the idea for Cubism.

Searching for a personal identity, she went to Augustus John's studio for advice about her painting. 'Don't go to Sickert—he'll only teach you how to paint pisspots,' he advised her. So she went on a cycling tour instead. It was an eventful trip, for when swerving to avoid a retired gondolier in Venice, she knocked down a flamboyant, red-headed and heavily powdered lady, wearing a rainbow-coloured hat. It was Lady Ottoline Morrell and, when she had recovered consciousness, the two took to each other at once.

It was Lady Ottoline's ambition to surround herself with people who would join her on an aesthetic plane filled with poetry and music. My grandmother joined this magic circle, making sketches of the people she met. She was strangely attracted by the Bloomsbury Group and became increasingly involved with the members.

She fell in love with the static, silent and inert Saxon Sydney-Turner; but it came to nothing. 'They were like two bookends, always kept apart by books,' observed Dora Carrington. My grandmother, like Saxon Sydney-Turner, seldom spoke. Amongst so many brilliant conversationalists she was therefore rather overlooked. Leonard Woolf recalled how she was even lost for words when she fell into a bog. 'I couldn't think of a wet enough adjective,' she later wrote in her diary.

However, she was always listening, watching and drawing. Unknown to the Group, she drew them constantly, often secreting her sketchbook

Maud with Friend by Rodin

Maud as The Three Graces by Munch

inside a copy of *Ermyntrude and Esmeralda*. The various members of the Group, often aloof and awkward with strangers, had no inhibitions in front of my grandmother. She was therefore able to record the unadulterated—or adulterated—truth.

After her marriage, she drifted away from the Group, brooding about some obscure quarrel, but she still observed them from her bijou residence in Camden Town. She never showed her drawings to anyone and it wasn't until her tragic death last year (when a hawk attacked her hang-glider) that they came to light. This sketchbook contains only a few of the thousands she made, but it gives a fresh, if unauthorised, version of that much-maligned circle and their friends.

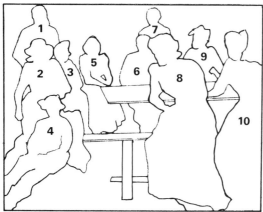

The Bloomsbury Group by Simon Bussy
1. Lytton Strachey
2. Lady Ottoline Morrell
3. Dora Carrington
4. Roger Fry
5. Maud Mahood
6. Maynard Keynes
7. Duncan Grant
8. Virginia Woolf
9. Leonard Woolf
10. Vanessa Bell

From Maud's Diary

Carrington had warned me about Virginia's latest time-saving gadget, her fireman's pole, but I thought she was exaggerating until I spent an almost entirely sleepless night at her place; every time I dozed off there was a loud thump and I woke with a start. That's the last time I'll stay with Virginia while she's in the middle of a novel . . .

Have just tottered back from Brunswick Square and yet another evening of Virginia insisting on reading from her diary. I really think such an occasion should be prefaced with a warning to the effect that all the characters mentioned are not entirely fictitious but bear little resemblance to anyone living or dead. How can anyone—never mind someone as ethereal as Virginia—lead a life with a scandal in every sentence?

Spent a busy morning sweeping white feathers away from Lytton's front door. Later, we all put in an appearance at Hampstead Town Hall to support his campaign to be registered as a Conscientious Objector. When he was asked by the military representative on the Tribunal, 'Then tell me, Mr Strachey, what would you do if you saw a German soldier attempting to rape your sister?', Lytton replied, 'I should try and come between them.'

What can I say about Lytton's knitting? To progress from mufflers for the troops to a tank-cosy is a tremendous achievement, so I am inclined to think that to turn now to producing penis muffs is a wicked waste of his talent.

Really, Lytton seems to spend more time thinking of Queen Victoria than actually writing about her. I suspect he imagines he *is* the old girl as he is apt to say, 'We are not amused' when there is any levity on the subject, and today I heard him remark, 'What a pity one can't now and then change sexes.' Tottering around on high heels doesn't seem to me to be an ideal way to try to find inspiration.

The pantomime at Garsington Manor was splendid this year. The usual squabbles over casting were skilfully avoided by Lady Ottoline who cast herself as the Wicked Fairy and everyone else as the Pantomime Horse, which gave Aldous Huxley (who wrote the songs) plenty of scope for sly aspersions. Despite a tendency to get lost in the bedrooms, the rear end of the horse gave a superb performance. Everyone agreed that it was the best pantomime ever. Lytton rather cryptically remarked that it must have been the first time that anyone had lost their virginity inside a panto horse . . . but he didn't say whose.

Now that most of my friends are registered as Conscientious Objectors—obliged to work on the land to help the war effort—I feel I must do my bit and support them. Despite my allergy to ducks, I bravely spent some time with them on the farm at Garsington and was fascinated by their efforts to disguise everything in sight. The camouflage seems quite effective—the herd almost indistinguishable from a Van Gogh.

Lady Ottoline has once again proved herself a superb hostess. Who else would take the trouble to sleep with every guest in turn? No wonder that every weekend poets, politicians and artists flock to Garsington Manor to be left to their own devices. There is something about the place that inspires people. I'm not sure what it is, but D. H. Lawrence always maintains that the plumbing has a strange effect on him.

Augustus John who is listening to...

Bertrand Russell who is pontificating to...

Saxon Sydney-Turner who is dozing beside...

E.M. Forster who is just aware of...

Vita Sackville West who is trying to ignore...

Leonard Woolf who is giving a lecture to...

Virginia Woolf who is writing gossip in her diary about...

Maynard Keynes who is pondering about...

Lytton Strachey who is knitting a witty scarf for...

Dora Carrington who is drawing...

HOGARTH PRESS

Katherine Mansfield who is sitting for...

Mark Gertler who is being discussed by...

Ralph Partridge and Gerald Brenan who have been reading...

W.B.Yeats who is reciting to... D.H.Lawrence who is seething about...

Ottoline Morrell who is entertaining...

Clive Bell who is flirting with...

Vanessa Bell who is decorating a firescreen made by...

Duncan Grant who is lending half an ear to... Roger Fry who is preaching to...

Pears' Soap

Inspiration striking Virginia during the night

Bedtime story : Virginia reads from her diary

The Tribunal for Conscientious Objectors was not impressed
by Lytton's specially hired pale-blue seat-cushion

Lytton trying to come between his sister and a German soldier

When Lytton tired of knitting mufflers for soldiers
and sailors he tried something more ambitious

Lytton contemplating the bust of an eminent Victorian while awaiting inspiration

Lady Ottoline stars in the annual pantomime at Garsington

Clive constructs a Post-Impressionist scarecrow

Lady Ottoline, wearing her cast-offs, deputises as a bird-scarer

Duncan, Vanessa and David camouflage the farm

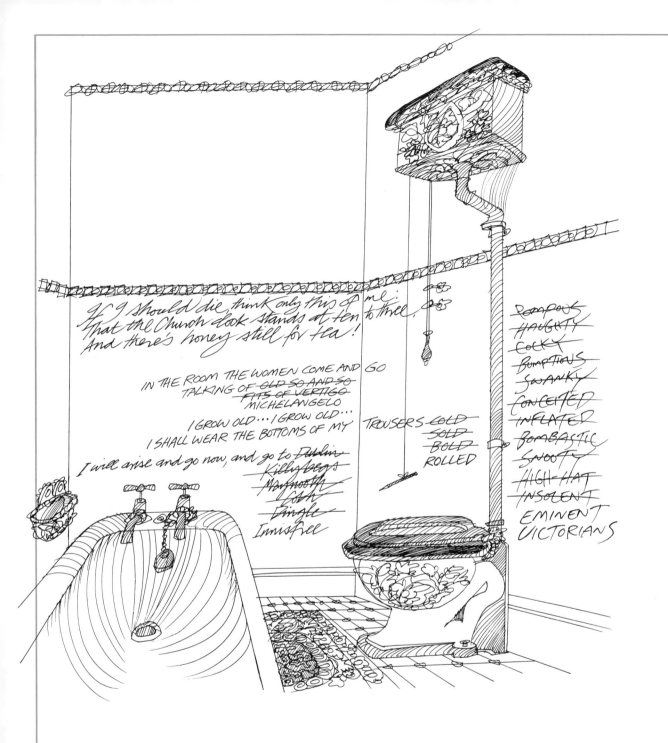

Poets' Corner, Garsington Manor

Maynard solves the lawn-mowing problem at Garsington
and the world's economic problems at the same time

Lytton was somewhat suspicious of new members

The members tended to deal harshly with any lapse of memory

From Maud's Diary

It's all very well Lytton belonging to The Apostles, a secret society that repudiates customary morals, conventions and traditional wisdom, but if all he wants to do is indulge in cushion fights, games of blind man's buff and inventing nicknames, why doesn't he go into politics?

I'm distinctly uneasy at every meeting of the Memoir Club. It's very difficult to read an autobiographical paper that has to be absolutely frank to friends like Clive and Lytton when you've got absolutely nothing to be frank about! Despite their promise not to be 'touchy', the Group was rather harsh on poor Saxon, I thought.

I am very excited to be asked by Roger Fry to do some designs for his new venture, the Omega Workshops—a place where young penniless artists can decorate furniture and other objects he can sell—but at the same time a trifle worried. How can I compete with chairs that have mechanical legs which follow you around, or indeed with a pedal-bin with a hand that comes out and removes the rubbish for you?

The Group maintain that they don't mind criticism, so I was a little surprised to see they had a Roll of Dishonour hung at the Omega Workshops. I'm sure Wyndham Lewis will be delighted to find his name at the top of the list.

Whenever I go to Durbins, Roger always asks me to count the dots in his Seurat to support some theory of his. Have got to seven thousand, two hundred and sixty-nine so far ... and only on one damn figure!

Perhaps they think I have hidden talent, but ever since Leonard and Virginia established the Hogarth Press they have been badgering me to come and work for them and in a moment of weakness I agreed. Spent all my time making up parcels of her latest novel, which is selling like hot cakes. Wasn't very good at it. Virginia was too busy writing to notice, but I have never seen anyone get into such a rage over an inept parcel as Leonard.

While Saxon was out of the room got a glimpse of his diary. He had only written five words in the last six months; and three of those had been rubbed out.

Went for a walk with Ottoline in the worst fog for thirty years. Got back safely; she had no difficulty finding her way as she has second sight. *The Times* next day reported that nine hundred and thirty-one people had stepped into the Thames.

Virginia was worried after Dr Craig had said her weight was too low for safety; however, by carrying some ballast around in her handbag she was able to put it to the back of her mind.

Lytton was rather peevish today. He has turned his ill health into a religion and wants us to become his disciples. My patience has worn so thin it is positively emaciated.

Saxon came over to discuss the meaning of structure and texture in Chinese poetry, but we spent a happy afternoon counting sugar lumps instead as he hadn't much to say.

I am full of admiration for the way Leonard has trained their dog to fetch Virginia's writing materials at the same time as her slippers.

THE OMEGA WORKSHOPS
After the opening, Roger Fry is forced to take
some precautions over the high-pitched Bloomsbury voice

Cigarette-holder for Virginia Woolf

Bird-bath for E. M. Forster

Sun-hat for Lytton Strachey

Reading lamp for
Katherine Mansfield

Library steps for Bertrand Russell

Sun-glasses for W. B. Yeats

Digital egg-timer for Maynard Keynes

Fresh flower hat
for Vita Sackville-West

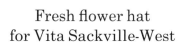

Pug umbrella for Lady Ottoline Morrell

Leonard and Virginia on the novel production line

Roger, Lytton and Vita trying to capture a rare specimen

Virginia doing the dishes after an intimate dinner with Vita

Virginia and Vita contemplate making history

From Maud's Diary

Virginia's friendship with Vita seems to be developing by leaps and bounds—mostly towards bed as far as I can see. She seems so taken with Vita's 'fullbreastedness in full sail on the high tides' that she is thinking of writing a book about her. I suspect Vita is only too keen to provide the plot.

Saw Vita at Long Barn on Sunday. 'Ah yes, my life's a compromise—all a compromise,' she said as she removed a Ming vase to give an air of austerity to the room; she didn't succeed, although I thought it was a good try.

Somehow I always feel slightly ill at ease at Charleston. Vanessa and Duncan are compulsive decorators. They spend all their time painting every window, wall and door with landscapes— you can't tell whether you are indoors or out. Very disconcerting when you are trying to find the bathroom. Personally, I think keeping chickens with their tails dyed red, white and blue is gilding the lily a bit.

Unfortunately, the Post-Impressionist show has had a rather unsettling effect on Roger. He sees significant forms everywhere he goes and insists that we do the same. This makes Lytton very tetchy as he doesn't think a sunset, a stag at bay or a nude boy should be treated in *exactly* the same way.

I used to enjoy picnics, but now that Roger sees them as works of art they have become rather tiresome. I find that nudity, jam sandwiches and wasps are incompatible.

Lady Ottoline has had a splendid idea: she has commissioned topiary statues of her friends, which has allowed her to give her garden an exotic new look and, in the case of Mark and Carrington, do a spot of matchmaking at the same time. I think she got the idea from Leonard's remark about Carrington: 'She had a head of the thickest hair I have ever seen ... it stood out like a solid, perfectly grown and clipped yew hedge.'

I could listen all day to W. B. Yeats talking about spiritualism; how he has made chairs and tables waltz and heard phantom taps in morse code. I believe it all but the bit where he says that when he is communing with the spirits he feeds them with bread and margarine.

One of the problems of staying at Garsington is Ottoline's sleepwalking. She always seems to end up in someone else's bed. While this is appreciated by some guests, it is rather disturbing for us light sleepers. Philip has tried all kinds of remedies, including a form of stocks at the end of their bed, but she even managed to pick the lock with her toes while she slept.

Such a summer for travelling—Vanessa took advantage of the cheap rates for groups, hired a coach and we toured all over Europe. Lytton is a somewhat erratic driver due to his habit of reading *Baedeker* as we go along. It's amazing how quickly the average foreigner can leap over a hedge. Saxon forgot his glasses and didn't see a single sight!

Just returned from our visit to Gerald Brenan in Spain, which Lytton summed up in one word— D E A T H. Most of the time he didn't know whether he was coming or going, but Gerald and Carrington seemed to have enjoyed themselves.

Charleston Farm, Sussex

For a time even Roger's picnics were influenced by Manet

Carrington by Mark Gertler

Bertrand Russell by Lady Ottoline

Virginia by Duncan Grant

D. H. Lawrence
by himself

Roger Fry by Augustus John

42

Maynard Keynes by Roger Fry

Clive Bell, Lady Ottoline and Leonard Woolf by Vanessa Bell

Lady Ottoline always tried to put W. B. Yeats's levitating to some useful purpose

Lady Ottoline liked to dress up as a shepherdess

The Group discover Lady Ottoline giving Henry Lamb an aspirin

Carrington, Ralph and Lytton on honeymoon in Venice

Lytton reading to Carrington and Gerald Brenan

Ménage à trois at Tidmarsh

A typical afternoon at The Mill House, Tidmarsh

Sometimes Lytton had to be coaxed to go for a walk

From Maud's Diary

I can't remember when Lytton said, 'I should love to be a Dowager Countess,' but when he is tired of pugs, cushions and erections there is nothing he likes more than dressing up. There is nowhere better than Garsington for this as Ottoline has more cast-offs than a moulting hen.

Quite enjoyed the latest fancy-dress party of Ottoline's—went as a chameleon and was delighted afterwards to hear that everyone thought I hadn't come.

Weekends at Garsington seem to be one long game of charades. I have the feeling that members of the Bloomsbury Group are all frustrated actors as they jump at any chance to enter the world of make-believe. It was rather sweet of Lytton to try and mime his one-day engagement to Virginia, but I think she rather overdid her act.

In Leonard's opinion, 'what cuts the deepest channels in our lives are the different houses in which we live.' If that is true, then the Bloomsberries have lived in some very odd houses. Actually I didn't mind the candles, the pump, the earth closet and the primitive cooking arrangement at Asheham, but I couldn't face the communal bath.

Virginia has likened the Group to a zoo. Now that members have become literary lions and developed a certain herd instinct, I have begun to notice how like certain birds and animals they really are. Carrington calls Lytton her 'Toad in the Hole' but I see him as something rather taller and languid.

Lytton came to dinner on Saturday. He was at his lowest ebb. Too shattered by the frailty of mankind to talk but he made some very eloquent gestures.

Virginia wants me to join the British Sex Society. From what she tells me they have surprisingly frank discussions about the deformity of Dean Swift's organ, self-abuse after death, sex as a spectator sport and whether cats use the W.C. I don't think I know enough to be a member.

I'm not amused by practical jokes, so I don't know why de Vere Cole is continually trying to persuade me to join him in another one like the 'Dreadnought Hoax'. This time he wants the Group to dress up in dinner jackets and masquerade as talking penguins at the London Zoo.

Annoyed by Clive's flirtatiousness, Vanessa has made and decorated a pair of blinkers for him. Now, much to her further annoyance, he insists on wearing them while he is philandering.

Saw Philip Morrell in his bright leather gaiters, double-breasted waistcoat and jewelled buttons go out to weed in the garden. He didn't make much progress and later Ottoline discovered that the ivy had begun to entwine his legs.

Virginia apart, the Group consider themselves as sane as a brush, yet occasionally they agree to be analysed by James Strachey in order to help him with his Freudian research. I find this very restful, but most of them attribute their bouts of manic depression to these sessions.

Life piles up so fast that I have no time to keep up with it, but I must note another of Lytton's anniversaries. Yesterday we all met at his chemist's shop to commemorate the first time he had a sip of his life-saving Sanatogen. No expense was spared and we all got very drunk.

DRESSING UP FOR A PARTY AT GARSINGTON

Lytton and Duncan

Leonard and Virginia

Vanessa and Clive

Lady Ottoline and Philip Morrell

53

CHARADES AT GARSINGTON

Leonard gives them an easy one

Virginia and Lytton give them a hard one

Maynard and Lydia improvise

Edith, Sacheverell and Osbert try to convey

Virginia does a
well-known symbol

the essence of Sitwellism

Visitors approaching Asheham House with apprehension

Bath night at Asheham

THE BLOOMSBURY ZOO

Virginia Woolf tuning up

Lytton Strachey thinking
of higher things

Lady Ottoline Morrell putting on a display

Saxon Sydney-Turner meditating

Roger Fry prickling at a critic

Leonard Woolf getting the hump

Clive Bell trying to digest
a new art movement

Desmond MacCarthy cogitating

E. M. Forster searching for
a new experience

Vanessa Bell keeping a low profile

Self-portrait of Maud waiting for a Bloomsberry to come into sight